GW00672162

SPRING HARVEST PRAISE **2011**

2 IN 1 SONGBOOK & DIGI-SONGBOOK

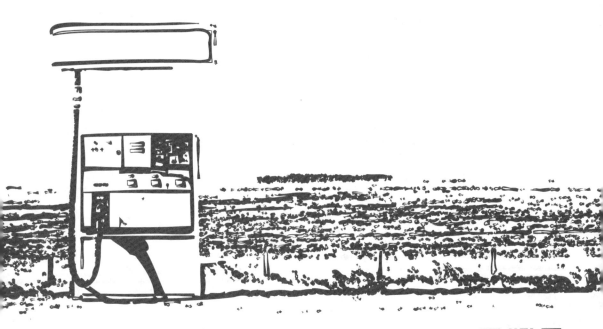

Equipping the Church for action

What's this?

On your phone, open your barcode reader app and scan the code here.

If you haven't got a barcode reader then search 'qrcode' in your apps store.

Copyright & Photocopying

No part of this publication may be reproduced in any form without the permission of the copyright holder of the songs and the publisher of the songbook. Exceptions to this rule are made for holders of licences issued by Christian Copyright Licensing International, as follows:

CHURCH COPYRIGHT LICENCE/COLLECTIVE WORSHIP COPYRIGHT LICENCE:
Churches, schools and organisations holding a church or collective worship copyright licence may reproduce and store the words of the songs within the terms of their licence.

For information about these licences visit www.ccli.co.uk.

MUSIC REPRODUCTION LICENCE/COLLECTIVE WORSHIP MUSIC REPRODUCTION LICENCE:
Churches, schools and organisations holding a music reproduction licence may photocopy the words and/or music of the songs directly from this publication within the terms of their licence.

FOR UK, IRELAND AND EUROPE:
Christian Copyright Licensing International Ltd.
Chantry House, 22 Upperton Road, Eastbourne,
East Sussex, BN21 1BF
www.ccli.co.uk

FOR USA AND CANADA:
Christian Copyright Licensing Inc,
17201 NE Sacramento Street, Portland,
Oregon, 97230 USA
www.ccli.com

FOR BRAZIL:
CCLI LICENCIAMENTO DE DIREITOS AUTORAIS Ltda.
Alameda Rio Negro, 1084 - Sala 75
CEP 06454-000 Barueri, SP Brasil
www.ccli.com.br

FOR ASIA PACIFIC:
Christian Copyright Licensing International
PO Box 6644, Baulkham Hills BC,
NSW 2153 Australia
www.ccli.com.au

FOR AFRICA:
Christian Copyright Licensing Africa (Pty) Ltd,
PO Box 2347, Durbanville 7551, South Africa
www.ccli.co.za

KEEPING WITHIN THE LAW

If your church musicians play direct from hymn books, such as this one, then the purchase price of each book pays the royalties due to copyright owners. However, if you wish to photocopy music for your musicians then you will normally need permission from the copyright owner(s). Alternatively you can obtain a Music Reproduction Licence* from CCLI which permits you to photocopy the words and music of hymns and worship songs from authorised** music publications. This licence also permits you to make customised musical arrangements for transposing instruments such as wind and brass provided the melody line remains unchanged.

* The Music Reproduction Licence is supplementary to the Church Copyright Licence, i.e. your church must hold both licences.

** An Authorised book is one which is covered by the Music Reproduction Licence. NB: Both the publication containing the song you wish to photocopy and the song itself must be covered by the Music Reproduction Licence.

For more information, contact CCLI on +44 (0)1323 436103 or visit www.ccli.co.uk.

UNAUTHORISED PHOTOCOPYING IS ILLEGAL and detrimental to the work and ministry of the songwriters and publishers.

All rights reserved. All songs are reproduced by kind permission of the copyright holders – names of which are shown below each song/hymn. Any omission of acknowledgement to composer or publisher will be corrected in future editions.

Prayers and liturgy have copyright details shown beneath them. They may be reproduced for local use with the indication of copyright, but not for resale without permission.

Acknowledgements

Music type-setting and new arrangements by David Ball
Guitar chord pages by David Ball & Becky Frith
Songbook cover design by Mark Prentice
CD-Rom artwork by Mark Steel
Songbook internal design & layout by Ascent Creative
Printed by Halcyon
CD-Rom authored by Cambron Software

Published & distributed by Elevation, 14 Horsted Square, Uckfield, East Sussex, TN22 1QG, UK.

Part of the Memralife Group, Registered Charity number 1126997, a Company limited by guarantee, registered in England and Wales, number 6667924.

Registered Office: 14 Horsted Square, Uckfield, East Sussex, TN22 1QG.

Spring Harvest wishes to acknowledge and thank the following people for their help in the compilation and production of this song book:

Leigh Barnard, Vicky Beeching, Dan Boreham, Pete Broadbent, Andrew Crookall, Jaqs Graham, Denise Hooper, Cheryl Jenkinson, Phil Loose, Karen Martin, Ruth Perrett, Sue Rinaldi and Rachel Whitney.

Thank you to Marie Birkinshaw, Mark Earey, Nick Harding, Sam Hargreaves, Chrissie Kelly, John Leach, Rebekah Long and Sharon Tedford for liturgy and Gerard Kelly for Twitturgy contributions.

Special thanks to Brenda Cameron and all at Cambron Software for Power Music Lite and your help in developing this resource.

ISBN 978-1-899788-75-0

Contents

The words edition of this songbook is
available in Braille and giant print

Discover the Spring Harvest Digi-Songbook

Over the years of the Spring Harvest songbook, there have been many helpful guest comments made which help us to refine our resource and hopefully deliver something more useful the following year. The one problem we've always struggled to solve is when a worship leader wants to play the song in a **different key to the book**. This may be because they need to sing it in a different register for male or female voice, or just drop it up or down a key to make it easier to lead. It may be that we want some songs to flow in a medley and to have them in the same key may help this to work.

This year, we are very excited to partner with Power Music and bring you the Digi-Songbook version of the Spring Harvest 2011 Songbook featuring the ability to **change the key of the guitar chords for every song.** Note that the music scores cannot be changed; maybe we'll be able to achieve this in the future!

Any of the songs can be printed out for your worship team or by utilising the software directly from a PC you can use monitor screens as "digital" music stands. You can build playlists for your church service, **search the songs by title, first line, scripture or theme** and also ensure that everyone is playing in the same key.

By going online you can see just how easy it is to use the Digi-Songbook powered by Power Music Lite. We recommend though that you upgrade from within the Songbook to the full version as this enables you to add your own songs as well as create your own categories and receive future updates.

To see the software working go to **www.springharvest.org/digisongbook** where you can see short videos to help get to grips with the software. As with all new software expect a small learning curve, but the intuitiveness of the software makes it easy to use and makes a huge difference to both worship preparation as well as 'live' worship leading.

Presently this software is Windows PC based but for Mac users we have also packaged the song scores and guitar chords as PDFs.

We trust this innovation for 2011 equips you to be even more effective in leading worship wherever God has called you to serve.

If you have any support issues on the programme, email Power Music on **info@cambronsoftware.co.uk**

SPRING HARVEST 2011
ROUTE 66

SPRING HARVEST
DIGI-SONGBOOK

POWERED BY *PowerMusiclite*
MUSIC MANAGEMENT SOFTWARE

Power Music Lite © 2011 Cambron Software
Customer Support: info@cambronsoftware.co.uk

Spring Harvest   COMPACT disc   elevation
CD-ROM
SHM1635B ℗ & © 2011 Elevation.
All rights of the Producer and the Owner of the recorded work reserved. Unauthorised copying,
hiring, lending, public performance or broadcasting of this recording prohibited.
www.elevationmusic.com

SPRING HARVEST
DIGI-SONGBOOK

POWERED BY *PowerMusic*lite
MUSIC MANAGEMENT SOFTWARE

INSTALL

Install the Spring Harvest Digi-Songbook

(Windows compatible)

UPGRADE

Upgrade to the full power of Power Music

- Add and edit your own songs
- Import from PDF
- Add your own categories
- Import/export songs
- Backup/Restore
- Receive free updates
- Save money when you upgrade from within Power Music Lite!

SINGLE LICENCE - £59.99
(NORMALLY £69)

5 PC LICENCE - £125.00
(NORMALLY £150)

10 PC LICENCE - £209.99
(NORMALLY £240)

MAC

Scores & chords for Mac

Alphabetical & Key Index

Song titles differing from first lines are in italics

All creatures of our God and King
(Praise him)

Key = B

Klaus Kuehn
& Thomas Miller

all the peo - ple praise___ him.___ Praise him,___

praise him,___ let all cre - a - tion sing.___

Wor - thy___ to re - ceive___ the glo - ry, ho - nour be - longs___

Mid section

1. All

to You; for - e - ver our King and Lord, all

praise be - longs to You.

MUSICIAN'S
NOTES

Be Thou exalted

Key = C

With feeling

Chris Eaton, Abby Eaton
& John Hartley

1. Be Thou ex - al - ted, for - e - ver and e - ver, God of e -
   al - ted, O Spi - rit e - ter - nal! Dwell in our

ter - ni - ty, An - cient of___ Days!___ Won - drous in
hearts and keep us ho - ly with - in;___ Oh, lead us

ma - je - sty,___ per - fect in wis - dom, glo - rious in
to Thy home and life e - ver - last - ing, o - pen Your

ho - li - ness, fear - ful in___ praise.
flood - gates and wel - come us___ in.

serves the least with jus - tice.
yearns to free the cap - tive soul.

Chorus

Lord have mer - cy, Lord have

mer - cy on us; Lord have me - rcy, break our stone cold

hearts.

3. Give me a heart hearts.

hearts.

Give me eyes to see
(The greatness of our God)

Key = E

Capo 2(D)

Jason Ingram, Stuart Garrard
& Reuben Morgan

Worshipfully

Giver of every breath
(All because of Jesus)

Key = C

With praise ♩ = 140

Steve Fee

Verse

Gi-ver of ev - 'ry breath I breathe, Au-thor of all e-ter - ni-ty,

gi-ver of ev - 'ry per - fect thing, to You be the glo - ry.

Ma-ker of hea - ven and of earth, no one can com -

- pre - hend Your worth, King o - ver all the u - ni-verse,

to You be the glo - ry.

God so loved
(Saviour of the world)

Capo 4(Em)

Key = G♯m

Rock feel

Ben Cantelon

Verse lyrics:

1. God so loved, that he gave his Son to lay down his life for the
(2.) spread the word of his soon return to re-claim the world for his

sake of us. He bore the weight of our sin and shame. With a
glo-ry. Let the church now sing of this com-ing King, crowned with

cry he said, 'It is fi-nished.' Christ the Lord, o-ver-came the
ma-je-sty: our Re-deem-er. And he reigns, ru-ler of the

dark-ness; he's a-live: death has been de-fea-ted. For he
hea-vens. And his name is Je-sus, the Mes-si-ah.

This song is recorded on the Spring Harvest 'New Songs 2011' album

made us a way, by which we have been saved. He's the Sa-viour of —— the world. ——

So —— we lift up a shout for his fame and re-nown. Praise the

Last time to Coda ⊕ | *1.*

Lord, praise the Lord: Je-sus, Sa-viour of the world. ——

D.C.(v.2)

2. We must

2.

Sa-viour of the world. Oh. ——

Christ the Lord o-ver-came the dark - ness, he's a-live: death has been de-fea - ted. And he

Sa - viour of the world.

Graffiti your grace on the walls of my life God. Finger-paint the words I need to see. Where warnings come may I read well.

Your word is a light to my path

Your word is a light to my path,
May it show me the way to You.
Your word is a glimpse of Your glory,
May it show me more of You.
Your word is a letter of love,
May it show me how to love You.

May the word of God live in us deeply
As we learn more of his love for us.
May the word of God live in us deeply
As we face challenges and trials.
May the word of God live in us deeply
As we consider our future plans.
May the word of God live in us deeply
As we hear his call and respond.
May the word of God live in us deeply
In all we do as we live for him.

Open our eyes to see the beauty of Scripture;
the poetry, the stories, and the images.

Open our eyes to see the expanse of Scripture;
the journey, the nations and the saints.

Open our eyes to see the vitality of Scripture;
the drama, the glory and the hope.

Open our eyes to see the message of Scripture;
the grace, the sacrifice, the love.

© Nick Harding

Hallelujah

Key = starts in D♭

Noel Robinson
& Donna Akodu

Slow gospel 4

1. Hal - le-lu - jah, hal - le-lu - jah, hal - le - lu - jah.

I a-dore You, pre-cious Sa-viour, hal - le - lu - jah.

2. Hal - le-lu-jah, hal - le-lu - jah is the song we sing,

give our voic - es, giv - ing prai - ses as we en - ter in.

3. You de-light, Lord, in our prai - ses, come in - ha-bit now.

He came in flesh
(Sinless Saviour)

Key = C

Tony Fisher, Matt Boswell
& Aaron Keyes

This song is recorded on the Spring Harvest 'New Songs 2011' album

heaven at his command, endured the cross for all sin.
blood we are bought, we are cleansed and redeemed. { He is
Lord, our God of war, this is our Saviour, our King!

Chorus

Jesus, sinless Saviour, the spotless Redeemer of

man. He is Jesus, God is with us: all glory, all

praise to the Lamb.   2. For God him- Lamb, oh.

Mid section

Hal - le - lu - jah, You reign, oh Je - sus, You

reign, oh Je - sus, You reign on high. Je - sus, You

reign on high. 3. When ve-ry Je - sus, You reign on high.

MUSICIAN'S
NOTES

He is like no one
(Jesus is King)

Key = G

Leigh Barnard &
Matt and Helen Gallagher

Moderate rock

This song is recorded on the Spring Harvest 'New Songs 2011' album

strong - er,___ migh - ti - er___ than him,___ Je - sus___ is King.___

And we will praise him,___ ho - nour,___ wor - ship,___

D.S.S. for chorus repeat

bow down___ be - fore___ Je - sus___ our Lord.___

Last time to Coda ⊕   *Mid section*

Wor - thy___ are You,___ no one

else can com - pare; ___ all we a - dore ___ is found ___ in You. ___

Ho - ly ___ are You, ___ all the glo - ry ___ and power ___

to the one ___ who was, ___ and is ___ and is ___ to come. ___

D.S. 𝄋 *Coda*

There's no one

23 Heaven, there's no sorrow in heaven
(Kingdom come)

Key = A

Rock

Andy Young

Here is love

Key = G

Words: William Rees (1802-1883)
Music: Robert Lowry (1826-1899)
Arr. & additional chorus: Matt Redman

1. Here is love, vast as the o-cean, lov-ing kind-ness as the
(2.) mount of cru-ci-fix-ion foun-tains o-pened deep and

flood, when the Prince of Life, our Ran-som, shed for us his pre-cious
wide; through the flood gates of God's mer-cy flowed a vast and gra-cious

blood.   1. Here is blood. Who his
                                         tide. Grace and

love will not re-mem-ber? Who can cease to sing his praise? He can
love, like migh-ty ri-vers, poured in-ces-sant from a-bove, hea-ven's

His blood upon the wood
(The Lamb has conquered)

Moderate rock

Key = G

Mike Pearson

1. His blood up-on the wood, for-give-ness flow-ing down, death has lost its sting, the Lamb has o-ver-come. The
2. Ex-al-ted to the throne, crowned with ma-ny crowns, for-e-ver he shall reign, the Lamb who is to come. The

Lamb has con-quered, the Lamb has

This song is recorded on the Spring Harvest 'New Songs 2011' album

con - quered,___ fol-low him,___ fol-low him.___

The_ Fol-low him,___ fol-low him,_

fol-low him,___ fol-low him.___

When You speak God, the earth trembles.
My heart, too, is stirred to hear Your words.
May I listen well and, listening, obey.

How can we forget that he has made his mercy known
(All that is in us)

Capo 3(D)

Key = F

With praise

Marty Funderburk
& Stephen Hinkle

1. How can we for-get that he has made his mer-cy known,
2. How can we for-get that he's our good and faith-ful friend,

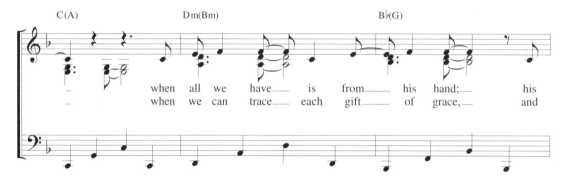

when all we have is from his hand; his
when we can trace each gift of grace, and

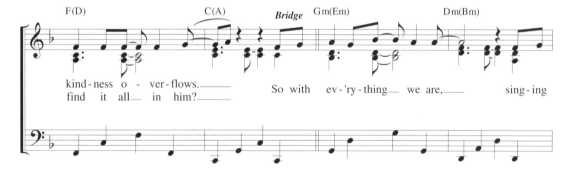

kind-ness o-ver-flows. So with ev-'ry-thing we are, sing-ing
find it all in him?

Bridge

from a grate-ful heart. We will bless the Lord,

Chorus

now and e - ver - more._____ We will

All that is in___ us; all that is in___ us;

all that is in___ us.

How could I not be on Your side
(Walk humbly)

Key = C

Lyrics: Nigel Briggs
Music: Trent

1. How could I not be on Your side, now You've shown me what it means to be alive? What can I give to show You how much You've changed me,

2. Seasons they change, passions they fade, but one thing's for sure: You will always remain. King of my heart, Jesus, You are always with me,

No-thing can se - par - ate— us from— our God.— For-

e - ver and e - ver You will— reign.—

Trent: Live at Spring Harvest

Spring Harvest is known for exuberant and heartfelt worship – Trent is known for authentic adoration and great songs that sing the story of God's love. Put the two together and what emerges is the wonderful sound of thousands of worshippers proclaiming devotion to a glorious God.

Taken from a week in the life of the 2010 event, immerse yourself in a climate of praise with well-known classics like *Did You Feel The Mountains Tremble* and *Friend Of God* alongside Trent favourites including *Perfect Sacrifice*.

How great is Your love
(All glory)

Key = A

Nikki Fletcher, Tim Hughes
& Martin Smith

Steady 4, building

1. How great is Your love, that ne-ver gives up on me;
2. So great is Your love, it keeps all its pro-mi-ses;

stron-ger than shame, car-ries me back
un-shak-a-ble, e-ter-ni-ty rests

to You.
in Your hands.

Je-sus, my Re-deem-er,
Je-sus, I sur-ren-der,

v.2 only

You have made a way.
lead me in Your ways.

This song is recorded on the Spring Harvest 'New Songs 2011' album

91

Beyond Songs: Getting Creative

by Abby Guinness

There are plenty of scriptural instances of music and singing; in praise, thanksgiving and celebration, in repentance, devotion and dedication. In Colossians 3:16 we're also reminded that 'psalms, hymns and songs from the spirit' should be used to 'teach and admonish one another with all wisdom.' In all aspects of our faith this is a vital activity, crucial to the Christian community.

However, of 254 occurrences where the word 'worship' appears in the Bible, only a small proportion makes reference to musical activity. That's not to say it didn't happen if it's not mentioned, the point is that worship is more than music. Perhaps the best definition is in Romans 12:1, 'Therefore, I urge you... to offer your bodies as a living sacrifice, holy and pleasing to God - this is your true and proper worship.' Our hearts, minds, souls and bodies in their entirety form our expression. That's why making music is so great, it can encourage us to engage them all. What's more... it's not the only thing that does.

Are there moments in our corporate worship when we can experiment? Could we explore different ways to offer God everything that makes us who we are? Could we aim to involve our other senses and break out of our usual routines? We don't need to get stuck in a 'block' of sung worship, many elements can be entwined and layered with music and song.

As a call to worship, try reading a Psalm like 117 as you begin playing. The congregation can declare truth from scripture together, shouting it loudly in triumph, or taking the time to commit it to memory. You could choose some verses from Psalm 118 and have the congregation join in with the repeated response that God's love endures forever. You can encourage the congregation to make a physical response if they are able, raising their arms higher with each response, or holding hands in solidarity, or taking up various postures of kneeling, sitting and standing. Try clapping rhythms or responses, branch out into knee-slapping and foot-stamping, you could make a body orchestra!

Touch and taste are often neglected, even though communion sets a perfect example. Try using appropriate songs as a form of liturgy for communion, the whole process could be set to music. Each person might take a squeeze of honey to taste as worship begins, reminding us that God's word is like honey on our lips, or be given a piece of clay to mould as a symbol of ourselves in God's hands as we worship.

The power of the visual is well-known; photography, video and live art can all play a part in engaging our senses as we look, and as we create. As well as using inspirational things to look at, try having an art wall that people can contribute to as they sing, or have someone sketch something to be filled in by collage. If you theme your song choices they could all pull together with the images you show or create.

We haven't even started on poetry, drama, sculpture, meditation and so much more besides, but getting started is usually more than half the battle. Think as much as you can of things people can do together, involvement is key. If you keep communicating clearly with the congregation, and encourage everyone to play a part, they will feel safe and confident to try new things. And if something goes wrong and everyone falls about laughing, what does it matter? Laughter is worship too.

Abby Guinness
www.livingandactive.co.uk

29

I believe in You

Key = A

Noel Robinson
& Donna Akodu

I belong to Father God

Key = A

Geraldine Latty

Moderately

Lord's prayer

Our Father who dwells in the heavens
and on the earth - You are Holy.

May heaven be a greater
present reality here on earth,

And may we choose to join
You in making that happen.

Provide us today with the
things that You think we need,

And may we not take for granted that
which You have already provided.

Forgive us when we
don't live as You intend,

And may we be ready to forgive
others when they don't live as we intend.

Guide us in Your wisdom away
from the things that would distort us,

And restore the parts in us
that are already distorted.

You are goodness, beauty and truth,

May Your love rule always.

Amen.

I come to seek the face of the Lord

Key = Gm

Capo 3(Em)

Luke Finch

Thoughtfully

I come to seek the face of the Lord,___ and I bow down on my knees;

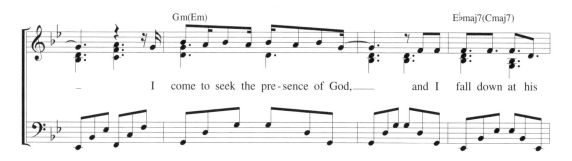

__ I come to seek the pre-sence of God,___ and I fall down at his

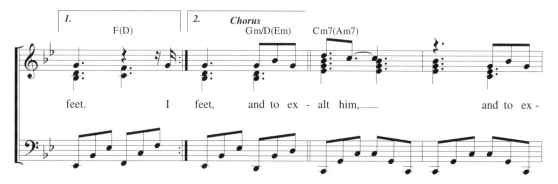

feet. I feet, and to ex - alt him,___ and to ex-

alt him:___ Ho - ly___ God. and to ex - alt him,___

More than feelings and flutterings, love is a
road we walk; a song we hear; a map marked
out. Guide us God in the way of love.

I have a hope so sure
(My God reigns)

Key = A

Matt Hooper
& Jonathan James

1. I have a hope so sure,___ an an-chor for___ my soul.
2. By faith, I have be-lieved___ and on His truth___ I'll stand:

My peace in the worst of times:___ I
no pow'r in___ life or death___ can

trust in God a-lone.___ Let ev-'ry
take me from___ His hand.___ Let ev-'ry

voice de-clare___ it now:___ (—) My God___
voice de-clare___ it now:___

My God —— My God is great - er,

my God is o - ver all. My God is great - er, my God is o - ver all.

Kids Praise Party 6 CD

This year's Kids Praise Party zooms into top gear with a thirst quenching collection of amazing songs and incredible grooves!

The 6th in this greatly celebrated series for young people builds on the strengths of all the others... with a combo of brand new and well-known worship songs to develop real faith and true knowledge about God and a music soundtrack from hi-speed to chillaxin, that will keep ears smiling, feet dancing and hearts in tune with the rhythm of a world-changing God!

Pre-school Praise 6 CD

Prepare for an amazing adventure as Pre-School Praise 6 presents a story-book of songs that will make feet stomp, voices sing, hands clap and at the same time, teach wonderful God-truths and fascinating facts about the Bible! With musical rhythms to shake the room and top tunes that are easy to remember, what a great way for young children to learn about Jesus!

PLUS: Kids Praise Party 6 Music Book

Featuring all the music scores to both Spring Harvest 2011 children's CDs.

 Available from EssentialChristian.com or your local Christian bookstore

I love Your presence

105

I see the cloud
(Show me Your glory)

Key = D

Nate Ward III, Kathy Frizzell
& Kim Walker-Smith

Slowly, building

We need wisdom as a driver needs fog lights.
As a miner needs a map. As a flight needs a
flight path. God of wisdom lead us.

35 I will give my whole self to You, Lord
(I worship You now)

Key = C

Brightly ♩ = 132

Marc James
& James Hellings

1. I will give my whole self to You,— Lord,

know-ing that Your heart is filled with— love.

I will trust my life to You, oh—— God,
2. One day soon the world will see Your—— face,

know-ing that Your grace will be e-nough.
sor-rows will flee, gone with-out a— trace.

This song is recorded on the Spring Harvest 'New Songs 2011' album

high and lift-ed up.____

We wor-ship You now,____   We wor-ship You now.____

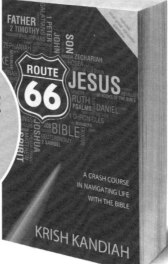

I will sing of my Redeemer

Key = E

Steadily

Chris Eaton
& John Hartley

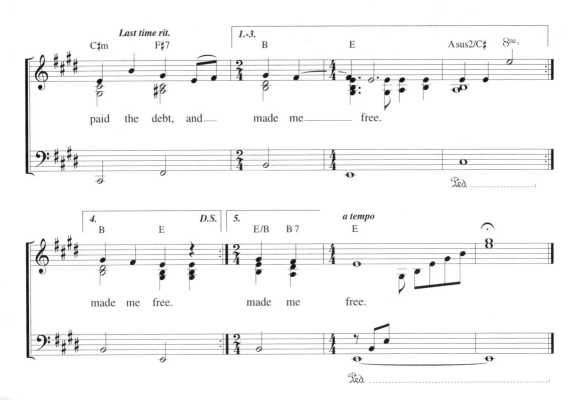

I'm standing at the cross
(Standing at the cross)

Key = G

Pete James

Steadily

I'm weak, You're strong

Key = C

Mark Tedder

Thoughtfully ♩ = 68

In our hearts, Lord
(Awakening)

Key = D

Chris Tomlin
& Reuben Morgan

121

Prayer for direction
Psalm 119:105

When our itinerary is confused
and we look for clarification

Your Word is a lamp to our feet

When our vision is impaired
and we seek a way forward

Your Word is a light to our path

When we reach the next junction
and study the signpost

Your Word is a lamp to our feet

When we gaze into the darkness
and wonder where to place the next step

Your Word is a light to our path

When we need to take our bearings
and the compass is unsteady

**Your Word is a lamp to our feet
and a light to our path**

© Marie Birkinshaw

Jesus, take me as I am
(Take me as I am)

Key = G

Luke Finch

Relaxed feel

I am wait-ing here____ Lord Je - sus as I am; and as I bow down in

this sur - ren - der, I am long-ing for You____ to come____ and take me___now.

Jesus, thank You for the cross
(Power of the cross)

Key = A

Martin Chalk

Rock

1. Je - sus, thank You for the cross, thank You for
2. Je - sus, my sal - va - tion's joy, paid the debt

— Your cleans - ing blood; washed a - way my sin, now
— of sin for all, washed me white as snow,

I'm for - gi - ven. You bring life where there is death,

You give peace for bro - ken - ess; I was lost

er to— be free.

won - der - ful— the cross— is.—

42 Jesus, thank You for the cross
(Worthy)

Key = D

Nick Drake, Becky Drake
& Ben Cantelon

Thankfully

1. Je - sus, thank You for the cross:
(2.) saved us from the e - ne - my,
3. Sa - viour, crowned in ma - je - sty,

You took our sin and
You tore down death, You
You reign in pow'r, the

healed our bro - ken - ness on that great day.
rose in vic - to - ry; up from the grave
world un - der Your feet, the ri - sen Son.

1. *2.,3.*

2. You our Sa - viour came.
the ho - ly One.

Bridge So I will

Jesus, You are strong to save
(We lift you up)

Key = A

Capo 2(G)

Brenton Brown

Moderately

1. Je - sus, You are strong to save,
2. For on - ly You have o - ver - come

there's no bat - tle You can't win; strong - er e - ven than
ev - 'ry trial this world can bring. Hum - bly You de - feat -

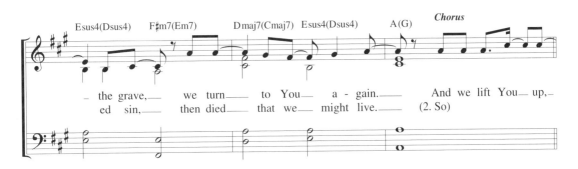

the grave, we turn to You a - gain. And we lift You up,
ed sin, then died that we might live. (2. So)

we lift You high - er, 'cause You de - serve our high - est praise.

Well sing it out, we'll sing it loud - er: Je - sus, name

a - bove all names.

Oh, we will lift You up, You con - quered temp - ta - tion,

o - be - di - ent to death. You won our sal - va - tion,

God of creation

from Genesis 1 & 2

Living God, who brought order out of chaos,
bring harmony to a fractured world.

Living God, who spoke light
into the darkness,
bring wisdom to a confused world.

Living God, who rested and
blessed the Sabbath day,
bring peace to a driven world.

Living God, who breathed life
into the human race,
bring hope to a despairing world.

© Mark Earey

47

Lost are saved
(Your great name)

Capo 3(G)

Key = B♭

Michael Neale
& Krissy Nordhoff

Steadily, building

1. Lost are saved, find their way, at the sound
find their strength at the sound

of Your great name; all con-demned feel no
of Your great name, hun-gry souls re-ceive

shame, at the sound of Your great name. Ev-'ry
grace at the sound of Your great name. The fa-ther-less,

fear has no place at the sound of Your great
find their rest, at the sound of Your great

This song is recorded on the Spring Harvest 'New Songs 2011' album

Choices

In every challenge there are choices

Lord may I choose for
Your kingdom every time

Above comfort
Above popularity
Above wealth
Above pride
For adventure
For courage
For kindness
For blessing

May my every decision line up, Lord,
with Your kingdom plans

May Your purposes prevail

May my thoughts and words and
actions honour You today.

© Chrissie Kelly

May Your voice be louder
(Full attention)

Key = A

Gradually building

Jeremy Riddle

50 More than just another song
(Listening)

Key = D

Vicky Beeching

Thougthtfully ♩ = 85

1. More than just a - no - ther song, more than one more
know Your heart, Lord, I want to

me - lo - dy; may - be what we need is si - lence,
know what moves You to un - der - stand what makes You weep,

may - be what we need is to be still, and lis - ten for the
to un - der - stand what makes You sing and smile. This will be my

still, small voice, 'cause we don't want to miss a whis - per,
life's one quest: to seek the One whose love has sought me;

just one word from You will bring me life. Just one word from You and

ev-'ry-thing chan - ges, just one word from You will bring me life.

bring me life, come and bring me life, how I

need Your life.

Intercessions on the Bible

Let us give thanks for God's written Word,
and let us pray for its power to be released into our world.
Lord, send forth Your word:
Let it not return empty.

We pray for those who work on the Bible:
For translators, academics, teachers and preachers,
that they may faithfully discern
and proclaim Your truth.
Lord, send forth Your word:
Let it not return empty.

We pray for those who read the Bible:
at home or in church,
in study, classroom or hotel room,
in hospital or in prison,
out of regular habit, deep need, or idle curiosity.
Lord, send forth Your word:
Let it not return empty.

We pray for those who scorn the Bible:
disbelieve it, discredit it, determine to disprove it.
We pray for those who have never read it
but don't believe it anyway.
We pray for those who find it difficult and oppressive,
those challenged by it who go away sorrowful.
Lord, send forth Your word:
Let it not return empty.

Lord send forth Your word
into a world which so desperately needs it.
Lord, send forth Your word:
Let it not return empty.
Amen.

© John Leach

51 My name is written on Your hands
(Counting on Your name)

Key = C

Tim Hughes, Nick Herbert
& Ben Cantelon

Moderately building ♩ = 75

161

O God of our salvation
(God of our salvation)

Key = C

Matt Boswell
& Michael Bleecker

Steadily flowing

Verse

1. O God of our sal-va-tion, who reigns up-on the throne;—
hold the Son, our Sa-viour, who for our sin was slain;—
God the Ho-ly Spi-rit, re-veal-ing de-i-ty;—

the sov-'reign Fa-ther, great is he from whom all bles-sings
the Christ, who pur-chased with his blood, the wret-ched souls of
the fount of life and love di-vine through-out e-ter-ni-

flow.
men.   O— God of—our sal-va-tion, from— whom re-demp-tion—
ty.

comes,   O— Fa-ther, Son— and Spi-rit, the bles-sèd three— in

This song is recorded on the Spring Harvest 'New Songs 2011' album

one.

2. Be one.
3. O

Mid section

As - cribe,   O church,___ the   great - ness and the

glo-ry due___ his   name,   one___ God, one be-ing one   es - sence, oh,   tri-une God pro-

claimed.   A -   men,_____   a -   men,_____   a -

men,_____   a - men.   A -   men.

163

On that dark night
(Emmanuel)

Key = A

Vicky Beeching

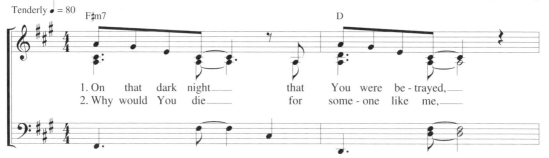

1. On that dark night that You were be - trayed,
2. Why would You die for some - one like me,

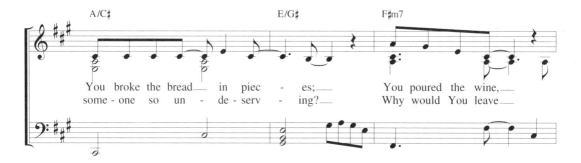

You broke the bread in piec - es; You poured the wine,
some - one so un - de - serv - ing? Why would You leave

know - ing Your life would soon be poured out to heal
hea - ven's glo - ry to step down and car - ry my bur -

- us: { what love is this? Em - ma - nu - el,
- dens:

This song is recorded on the Spring Harvest 'New Songs 2011' album

MUSICIAN'S
NOTES

One day when heaven was filled
(Glorious day)

Key = D

Michael Bleecker

1. One day when hea - ven was filled with his prais - es; one day when sin was as bleak as could be, Je - sus came forth to be born of a vir - gin, he dwelt a - mong men, my ex - am - ple is he!
2. One day they led him up Cal - va - ry's moun - tain, one day they nailed him to die on the tree; suf - fer - ing an - guish, de - spised and re - jec - ted, bear - ing our sins, my Re - deem - er is he!
3. One day the grave could con - ceal him no lon - ger, one day the stone rolled a - way from the door; then he a - rose o'er death he had con - quered; now is as - cen - ded, my Lord e - ver - more!
4. One day the trum - pet will sound for his com - ing, one day the skies with his glo - ries will shine; won - der - ful day, my be - lo - ved ones bring - ing; glo - ri - ous Sa - viour, this Je - sus is mine!

2° D.C (v.3)

This song is recorded on the Spring Harvest 'New Songs 2011' album

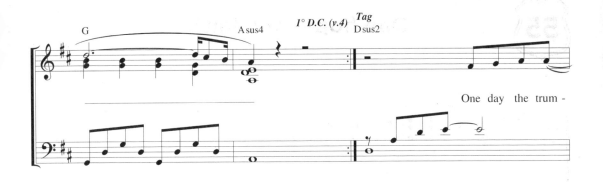

One day the trum-

-pet will sound for his com - ing, one day the skies

with his glo - ries will shine.

Switch-on my desire for discovery, God.
New depths of love. New deeds of mercy.
New delights in who You are calling me to be.

One hope, one faith

Key = E

With strength

Noel Robinson
& Donna Akodu

Chorus

One hope,— one faith,— one Fa-ther by which— we are saved.

One pur - pose, one mind:—

After v.3 Chorus to Coda

Je - sus is the hope of man-kind.—

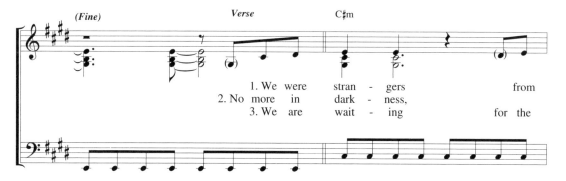

(Fine)   *Verse*

1. We were stran - gers   from
2. No more in dark - ness,
3. We are wait - ing   for the

Open my eyes again to see
(Arise)

Capo 4(G)

Key = B

Moderately

Becky Frith

1. O-pen my eyes a-gain to see the won-der of You,
that we might live see-ing the full-

Your life in me Your glo-rious strength
-ness of this gift; streng-thened, em-pow-

that works with-in: Lord, o-pen my eyes.
-ered, trans-formed with-in: Lord, o-pen our eyes.

1. F♯(D)

2. F♯(D)

2. O-pen our eyes

57 Open my eyes so I will walk
(Surrender)

Key = E

♩ = 142

Stuart Barbour

Verse

O - pen my eyes so I will walk a hum - ble life of thank -
life of hope, a voice of praise, a ser - vant heart that's full

- ful - ness, liv - ing by faith in sur - ren - der to You, Lord.
- of grace, bless'd to live ac - cord - ing to Your word.

1.

A

2. Bridge

Keep me in time with the rhy -

- thm of Your heart, let Your word be the strength

Of my soul——

Our God is mercy

Key = A

Cpao 2(G)
With energy

Brenton Brown, Eoghan Heaslip
& Nick Herbert

3rd time to Mid section
Last time to Coda

How important are the words?

by Graham Kendrick

When I was recording Meekness and Majesty, I showed the text to a friend who holds a theological degree. Affirmative nodding of the head turned to concerned shaking, and he muttered something to the effect that this could get me into trouble! In my search for an image to convey Christ being born as a human being, I had opted for 'clothed in humanity'. My friend pointed out that clothes are taken off as well as put on, and this appeared to contradict the truth that Christ became permanently human and reigns now in his resurrected and glorified human body. Furthermore the idea that Christ was made temporarily human was a well-known heresy, and did I really want to revive it! I found an alternative line and escaped the modern equivalent of being burned at the stake.

Theology is simply the study of God, and everyone who opens their mouth to sing or speak about God, inevitably expresses an idea about God, a theology; the question is, whether it is a good one or a bad one, a true or a false one. Every song sung in Christian worship has a theology!

It is not that our existing songs are full of grievous errors! In my view the pressing issue is one of balance; it is about what is missing, the subjects we never sing about because the songs are either not written, or not chosen. And it is about the growing dominance of a 'default' worship culture that only allows for certain kinds of expression, a limited range that edits out certain subject matter. So, why does any of that matter?

God's Glory

Orthodoxy sounds like a dusty old word, but actually it means right glory, in other words representing God as he actually is. A large part of worship's purpose is to lovingly and accurately describe God's nature and qualities. The New Testament shows us that the early church had a continuous and serious battle with false teaching and the encroachment of the worlds thinking. That battle is a fierce as ever, and perhaps more than ever, our worship songs are on the front line.

The uniqueness of the Gospel

NT Wright says: 'The place of doctrine within Christianity is absolutely vital. That's why we say the Creed at the heart of our regular liturgies: we are defined as the people who believe in this God. We need theology, we need doctrine, because if we don't have it, something else will come in and take its place.' (For all God's worth, Wm B Eerdmans Publishing Co.)

Keeping perspective

However, it is important to keep perspective. Songs are not designed to be exhaustive theological treatise; they use poetical devices like imagery to paint pictures on the imagination – think for example of the power of Isaac Watts 'When I survey the wondrous cross.' Whilst being alert to the accuracy of words we should not legalistically search for theological transgressions. Songs are imperfect, just like their composers and the congregations who sing them, and God is gracious enough to make good use of imperfect things, so let's be gracious too.

Graham Kendrick
www.grahamkendrick.co.uk

59 Our hope is in You, Lord
(Our hope)

Key = G

Steady gospel feel

Geraldine Latty

191

Praise Your name
(King of all grace)

Key = A

Rock ♩ = 129

Marc James

Verse

1. Praise Your name, we praise Your name, with a pas-sion-ate sound, with an in-ti-mate cry,
2. Praise Your name, we praise Your name, for all that You've done in the black-est of nights

1. to the King of all grace.

2. You're our ris-ing sun.

Chorus

Vic-to-ry,

with us - for the poor and the faint. With us - for the vic - tim a - fraid.
with us - for the wor - ker un - paid. With us - for the child like a slave.
with us - to be good news to - day. With us - to be com - fort in pain.

With us - for the home - less a - gain.
With us - for the land that longs for rain.
With us - to an - nounce a bet - ter way.

Yes, our God of love, our God is

great.

So beautiful
(Jesus' name)

Key = G

Ryan Delmore
& Jim Folkrod

Moderately ♩ = 78

Lyrics:
So beau-ti-ful,____ no name is___ high-er, so won-der-ful____ is Je-sus'____

1. name.
2. name, is Je-sus'____

name. Ev-'ry knee____ will bow____ in hea-ven and____ the earth;____ and ev-'ry eye____ will see____

Spirit of God

Steadily

Key = G

Stuart Barbour

sus.   I will help the poor,   love my neigh-bour more,   I sur-

Last time to Coda ⊕   **1.**   **D.C.**   **2.,4.**   **D.S.**

ren-der to my Lord, my   Sa - viour.   viour.   I will serve the

3.

viour.   Serve the King,_____   come serve the

King.   Serve the King,_____

come serve the   King._____   I will serve the

We are formed of stardust; conceived in a mind that set solar systems spinning. Tiny as we are, our meaning is magnificence.

69

Stand, kneel, bow
(Let our God be praised)

Key = B

Capo 4(G)

Michael Farren, Barry Weeks
& Chad Cates

The air is filled with angels
(Blessing and honour)

Capo 3(D)

Key = F

♩. = 59

Vicky Beeching,
Johnny & Sarah MacIntosh

1. The air is filled with an-gels, who speak and shout Your name, the at-mos-phere is chang-ing, as e-ter-ni-ty in-vades. And sud-den-ly a-bove us, the floor of hea-ven breaks;

2. One day we will see You, shin-ing like the sun; face to face with beau-ty, eye to eye with love. Stand-ing with the el-ders, we will throw our crowns

as Your Spi - rit falls down_____ we will
at the feet of Je - sus,_____ as we

Chorus

say: Bless - ing and_____ ho - nour,_____ glo - ry and_____ pow - er_____
shout:

be to Your name,_____ be to Your name._____ All of the_____ prai - ses_____

_____ through - out the_____ a - ges_____ be to Your name,_____ be to Your name_____

_____ for - ev - er - more.

The heavens declare
(You shall reign)

Capo 2(Em)

Key = F♯m

Ben Jones

1. The hea - vens de - clare,___ You are___ God;
2. You go be - fore,___ You will___ last,

the won - der of You___ in my___ heart.
the work of Your hands___ in my___ past.

And it leads me to say___ in e - ve - ry way:

You shall___ reign o - ver all___ of my___

life, You shall___ reign o - ver all___ of my___ life, o - ver

This song is recorded on the Spring Harvest 'New Songs 2011' album

73

The Lord is my shepherd

Capo 3(D)

Key = F

Moderately ♪ = 160

Kate Cooke

This song is recorded on the Spring Harvest 'New Songs 2011' album

There is a King
(Arise and sing)

Key = A

Brightly

Brenton Brown, Jason Ingram
& Marty Sampson

There's a new day dawning now
(Jubilee)

Lyrics: Nigel Briggs
Music: Trent

75

Key = G

Rock

1. There's a new day dawn-ing now,_____ a young_
   time of ju-bi-lee._____

new song sing-ing out;_____ a ri-ver deep and wide,_
— and old_____ set free;_____ and blind eyes now can see_

___ his love is all__ a-round,_____
___ God is on__ the move,_____

his love is all__ a-round,_____ God is all__ a-round._____
God is on__ the move,_____ his love is on__ the move._____

76 These mountains are high
(It's Your love)

Key = E

Luke Finch

Moderately

1. These moun-tains are high,___ but Your grace___
life is a path___ that keeps___
bur-den is light___ but I feel___

___ is great-er; these val-leys are deep,___
___ on wind-ing, and all I can do___
___ I'm dy-ing; los-ing___ my___ life

but Your heal-ing's deep-er. I
is Your truth___ be-lieve___ in. I
and then Yours___ I'm find-ing. I can-

And I can - not run,____ I can - not hide,____ I can't e - scape____ Your in - ces - sant____ love;____ Your love, Your love Your love is chas - ing me. Oh, I can - love is____ chas - ing me.

77 These walls, these streets
(For the glory of Your name)

Capo 3(G)

Key = B♭

Mark Tedder

Steadily ♩ = 86

Verse

These walls,_____ these streets,_____ these gates_____ are__ Yours._____ This church,_____ this town,_____ this land_____ is Yours._____ These hands,__ _____ this heart,_____ this life_____ is Yours._____ This is what we've been called_____ to; this is what You re-quire._____

Though I walk through waters

(Refuge)

Capo 3(G)

Key = B♭

Steadily ♩ = 80

Vicky Beeching

2. Ev-'ry-where You send me, an-gels will de-fend me:

Verse B♭(G)　　　　　　　F/A(D)

1. Though I walk through wa-ters, they won't o-ver-whelm me;

guard-ing me from dan-ger and ev-'ry snare.

Cm7(Am7)　　　　　　Gm(Em)　　　　F(D)

though I stand in fire, I won't be con-sumed.

Though the bat-tle's fierce, I know that You are near, so

Cm7(Am7)　　　　　　B♭/D(G)

Though I walk through val-leys with dark-ness all a-round me,

237

239

79 Through the love of God our Saviour
(All will be well)

Key = F

Original words: Mary Peters adpt. Leigh Barnard
Music: Leigh Barnard

241

pect a bright___ to- mor - row, all will___ be___ well;___ faith can

D.S. (al Coda)

sing through days___ of sor - row, all, all___ is___ well.___ On our

Coda

all_____ will___ be well,___

will be well.___

Through You, the blind will see
(I am free)

Key = C

Jon Egan
& Peter Furler

♩ = 136 C *Verse*

1. Through You, the blind will see, through You the mute
2. Through You the king - dom comes, through You the bat -

Fsus2

will sing, through You the dead will rise,
- tle's won, through You I'm not a - fraid,

Am

through You all hearts will praise, through You the dark -
through You the price is paid, through You there's vic -

Gsus4   F/G

- ness flees, through You my heart screams 'I am free!'
- to - ry, be - cause of You, my heart screams 'I am free!'

243

Last time to Coda 𝄌

C

I am free!____   I am free!____

1.   *D.C. (v.2)*   2.   *Mid section*

Am7

He who_ the Son____ sets free is

G   1.   C

free in - deed:_   I am free!____   I am free!_

2.   C   *D.S. al Coda*

I am

𝄌 *Coda*

C

245

To God be the glory

Key = B♭

Capo 3(G)

Original words: Fanny J. Crosby (1820-1915)
New music: Nathan Fellingham

With strength ♩ = 124

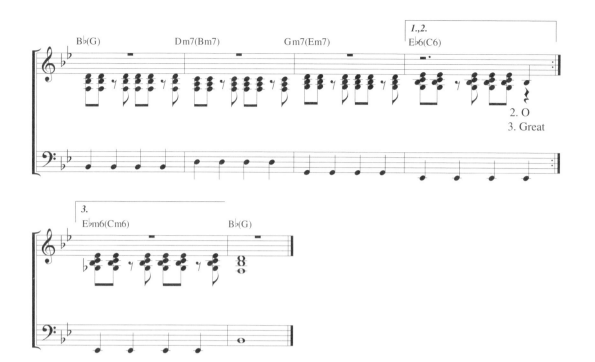

22 NEW SONGS FOR THE CHURCH
SPRING HARVEST 2011

Creative, inspiring and Bible-rich....
the latest in our series of 'New Songs'
wonderfully fulfils our desire to
resource the church with some of the
best songs from this year's Spring
Harvest songbook. Twelve songs are
given the full music workout – sparkling
guitars, beautiful strings and glorious
beats, whereas ten others are clothed in
more acoustic attire and are stunning in
their simplicity!

Once again this excellent collection of
worship songs, selected from a variety
of writers and covering a wide range of
styles, is a perfect source of spiritual
nourishment and a great way to
musically equip churches and
individuals!

**Available from
EssentialChristian.com
or your local Christian bookstore**

To him who is able

Key = A

With conviction

Lou and Nathan Fellingham
& Gary Sadler

Prayer is God's arc-welding. Love leaping.
Heaven earthed. Kingdom sparks across the
gap between what is and what can be.

To the cross I look
(Sweetly broken)

Key = B

Capo 4(G)

Jeremy Riddle

Rock

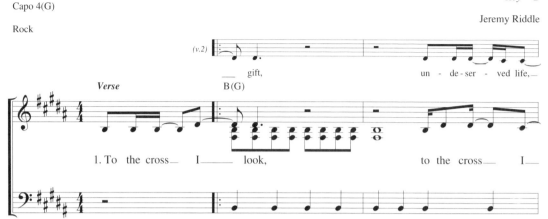

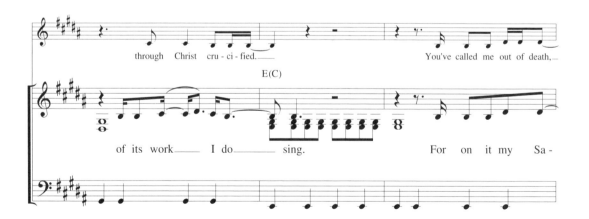

how won-drous Your re-deem - ing love and how great is Your faith - ful - ness.

God is not good, he is goodness. He is not loving, he is love. Defy my definitions, God. Mould my meaning to Your majesty.

Water You turned into wine
(Our God)

Key = A

Matt Redman, Jonas Myrin,
Chris Tomlin & Jesse Reeves

Moderately

1. Wa - ter You turned in - to wine,
2. In - to the dark - ness, You shine;

o - pened the eyes of the blind; there's no - one like You,
out of the ash - es, we rise. There's no - one like You,

none like You.
none like You.

Our God is great - er,

our God is strong - er; God, You are high - er than a - ny o - ther.

This song is recorded on the Spring Harvest 'New Songs 2011' album

Our God is heal - er, awe - some in pow - er, our__ God,__ our__ God.__

2° & 4° D.S. (al fine)   1.   D.C. (v.2)
Esus4 (Fine)   F#m   D   A   Esus4

2.
F#m   D   A   Esus4

Mid section
F#m   D

(__) And if our God is for us   then who could ev - er stop us,

A   Esus4

and if our God is with us   then what could stand a - gainst?__

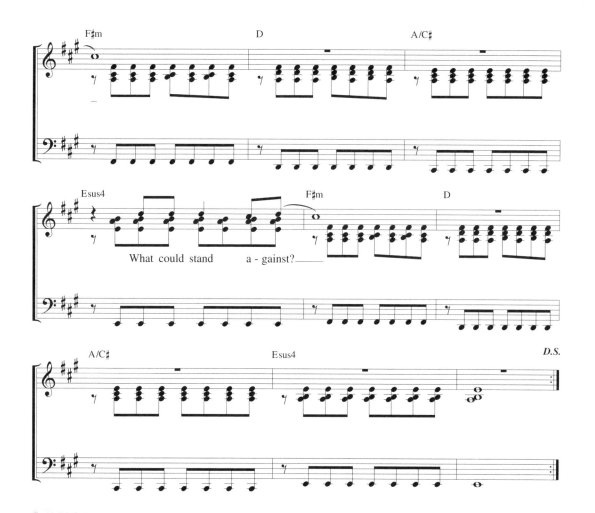

What could stand a - gainst?

Word of God liturgy

Father, when I come to You hungry,
Perhaps it's because I haven't fed
properly from Your word.
Word of God, feed me.

There are times when I lose my way;
I feel like I'm going round in circles,
unsure of my next step.
Word of God, lead me.

When I'm stuck in repetitive habits,
I know that You have more for me
outside of this mediocrity.
Word of God, shake me.

Parts of my heart are cold
towards the world You love.
Fill me with Your compassion.
Word of God, break me.

"The word of God is living and active,
sharper than any double edged sword."
**Feed me with Your wisdom,
lead me with Your love,
shake me with Your reality,
break me with Your perspective
and rebuild me with Your Holy Spirit's power.
Amen.**

© Sharon Tedford/Sam Hargreaves/engageworship.org

85 We are waiting and anticipating
(Thy kingdom come)

Key = D

Noel Robinson
& Donna Akodu

261

When I bend beyond belief, God my God is still God. When doubt is joy's jailer and fear faith's thief, God my God is still God.

We wait in hope for You
(Unfailing love)

Capo 4(G)

Key = B

Lyrics: Nigel Briggs
Music: Trent

Seriously

We wait in hope for You, our shel-ter and our truth.

You are al-ways faith-ful to Your Word.

Con-sume our hearts and minds, and be the au-thor of this life.

Your king-dom come, Your will be done.

(2° You are) In these times of doubt and sor-row, peo-ple need a

This song is recorded on the Spring Harvest 'Wonderful Saviour - New Songs 2008' album

When col-oured dreams_____ fade_ to grey_____ un - fail - ing love._

_ When the night_____ crowds out the day,_____ un - fail - ing love._

_ When there's no words left_ to say_____ God's

love re - mains,_____ oh, You_ re - main._

266

We will dance, we will dance
(For Your glory)

Key = B

Capo 2(A)

Moderately paced ♩ = 136

Ben Cantelon
& Matt Redman

We're not ashamed
(Not ashamed)

Key = E

Capo 2(D)

Ben Cantelon
& Nick Herbert

Moderately

1. We're not a - shamed of the one
(2.) - ing back, now to live

we love; there's a King of love who takes
for You; and tell the world it's true – You're the one

a - way our shame. The cross
and on - ly way. No back-

of Christ is our vic - to - ry;
- ing down, let the streets re - sound:

271

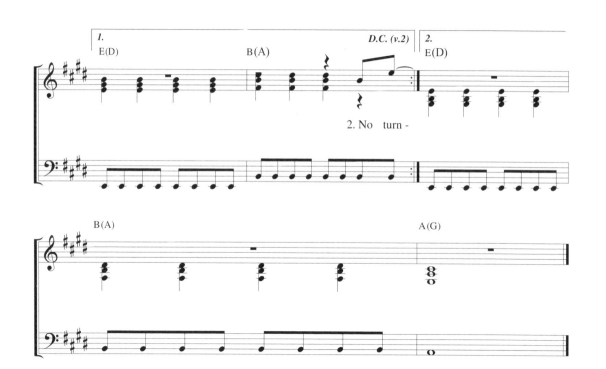

What can separate me from Your love
(Power of Your love)

Key = D

Gospel feel ♩ = 136

Noel Robinson
& Donna Akodu

What can we say?
(We adore You)

Key = C

Steadily, building in strength

Mike Pearson

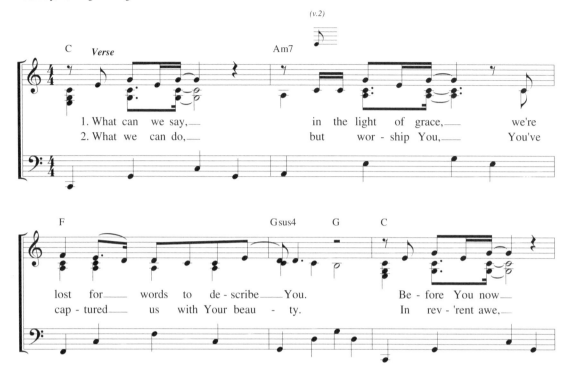

1. What can we say, in the light of grace, we're lost for words to describe You. Before You now
2. What we can do, but worship You, You've captured us with Your beauty. In rev-'rent awe,

we're o-ver-whelmed, by all Your kind-ness and glo-ry.
we'll love You Lord, with all our hearts we a-dore You.

Chorus

Lost in won-der we bow down, o-ver-whelmed by love and ma-je-sty;

for there is none— so beau-ti-ful:—

songs of love— will fill— e-ter-ni-ty.— We a-dore—

— You, we a-dore—— You.

We a-dore—

When my soul is weak
(My praise overflows)

Key = B

Jamie Rodwell
& Tom Field

Capo 4(G)

Gradually building

1. When my soul is weak, You bring strength for me.
(3.) run this race, on - ly by Your grace,

When the dark - ness clouds, You're the light I see.
You will lead me home to where I be - long.

When all hope seems lost, I re -
(2.) emp - ty and dry, hurt - ing and
My hope - se - cure in Your name; no more

mem - ber Your cross, when I'm strug - gling and bound,
bro - ken in - side, I can call on Your name:
hurt, no more pain. I am for - e - ver Yours,

278

the on-ly one who's wor-thy of praise, who con-quered death and

rose from the grave, oh, how I love You. Je-sus, I love

1.
You. To my

2.
You. Oh, how I love You, Je-sus, I love

You. Oh, how I love You, Je-sus, I love You. My

Coda
depths of my soul.

God is great among the nations

from Malachi 1:11

From beginning to end
You are great among the nations.

From daybreak to nightfall
You are great among the nations.

From east to west
You are great among the nations.

Great God of many nations,
of all times and all places,
accept the offering of our
strength and our weakness,
our beginnings and our endings,
our youth and our age,
to be used to bring Your rule in this world
and Your eternal reign nearer, day by day.

Amen.

© 2010 Mark Earey

Worthy is the Lamb
(Revelation song)

Key = D

Slow 4 ♩ = 60

Jennie Lee Riddle

2. Clothed in rain-bows of liv-ing co-lour,
3. Filled with won-der, awe-struck won-der,

1. Wor-thy is the Lamb who was slain;

flash-es of light-ning, rolls of thun-der.
at the men-tion of Your name.

ho-ly, ho-ly, ho-ly is he.

Bless-ing and ho-nour, strength and glo-ry and pow-er be
Je-sus, your name is pow-er, breath and liv-ing wa-ter,

Sing a new song to him who sits on

This song is recorded on the Spring Harvest 'New Songs 2011' album

You are all my heart longs for
(Presence)

Key = C

Kathryn Scott

Tenderly ♩ = 62

Verse

You are all my heart longs—— for,—— the trea-sure and—— the

hun-ger;—— I've tas-ted and—— I must have more—— of Your pre - sence,

1. God. You are God. *2.* **Chorus** You call me deep-

-er—— than be-fore;—— I'm fall - ing fur - ther—— in-to You, God.——

You are just so beau - ti-ful:—— I love Your pre - sence,——

You are God above the stars
(Grace)

Key = G

Lyrics: Nigel Briggs
Music: Trent

Moderately ♩ = 152

1. You are God a-bove the stars,
2. You are God who fills the skies,

and yet You choose to come in - to my heart.
and yet I feel that You're here with me now.

(v.2)

And in Your hands are o - ceans wide,
And in Your hands are moun - tains high,

and yet I feel that Your hand is in mine.
how I feel love, yes I feel love.

You are good
(Forever reign)

Key = C

Reuben Morgan
& Jason Ingram

Gradually building

This song is recorded on the Spring Harvest 'New Songs 2011' album

289

My heart will sing no o-ther name, Je - sus, Je - sus.

SPRING HARVEST 2012
A 6-day break that will refresh and change yo

"The phrase I hear time and time again from people who've been to Spring Harvest is **'it changed my life'** and that's what the Bible teaching does!"
Rob Parsons

- **Inspirational Bible teaching**
- **Vibrant worship**
- **Specialist-led children's & youth programme**
- **Free leisure activities**

www.springharvest.org

Spring
Harvest
Equipping the Church for

Rehearsal and spontaneity

by Mark Edwards

When I began thinking about writing this article, I found my mind running away. There were so many things I wanted to say, far too many to contain within the allocated 500 words.

There is plenty of practical advice I could offer on both topics. Rehearsal for instance; get rid of the drum screens and the 'in ears', (which inhibit communication); set up in a circle, where everyone has good eye contact; play quietly when first trying out an arrangement or new song, (if you can't hear what everyone else in the band is doing - then you're either playing too loud or too much!); think about arrangements ahead of time and come with clear charts, etc.

As for spontaneity; watch your worship leader like a hawk; have clearly defined signals that everyone is aware of, for such moves as "repeat this section, bring it down, go to the bridge"; listen to what is going on around you at all times; practise playing by ear at home to improve improvisational skills, I could go on.

But my hunch, given the above title, is that I am being asked to comment on and hopefully dispel the myth that somehow rehearsal, or too much preparation may stifle or inhibit freedom and spontaneity.

Since I was a child I have loved jazz music. You may not. Some say "where is the melody?" To me, jazz is packed full of melodic as well as harmonic and rhythmic invention. One of the things that drew me into this music was the impression that often the music sounded so together, almost rehearsed, and yet the players were improvising. There seemed to be total UNITY but total FREEDOM simultaneously. This is group improvisation.

When playing in a band, we should be practising the relationship values we aim for in general life. Principally humility. As we play music we need to be listening to one another, submitting to one another: if my part clashes with yours I may need to adapt.; supporting one another, flowing as one to create something beautiful. Where there is UNITY, God commands his blessing.

Rehearsal does not inhibit or stifle the possibility of freedom or indeed collective spontaneity. Quite the opposite is true. When we come together to rehearse we are looking to find the best way to serve a particular song. We are looking to find a part, which complements what everyone else is playing. When we have practised that part, we allow ourselves more freedom to focus on God during the worship time. And when we are aware of what the other musicians will be playing we have a much greater chance of being able to contribute something spontaneous, and yet congruous with the whole. When we rehearse we are preparing a platform, a launch pad for our worship.

You see, playing or singing something spontaneous does not mean suddenly launching into a solo, which rides roughshod over everything else. What we are looking for is a COLLECTIVE spontaneity! Group improvisation under the influence and prompting of the Holy Spirit! A spontaneity which breathes, and allows space for one to contribute an individual act of personal worship here and there with the full consent and blessing of the whole group. Worship leader, band, congregation and ultimately God, altogether in perfect UNITY and FREEDOM of expression.

Of course another great benefit of rehearsal is that we spend time together as human beings; we develop relationships; we have fun together, which has a huge impact on how we will operate as a team.

Music is a most wonderful gift and powerful tool given to us by the Lord. We should approach the practise of it with much respect, reverence, thoughtfulness and joy as we come together to offer back to him in perfect, unified, spontaneous love and worship.

Mark Edwards

Mark Edwards is the Producer of this year's Spring Harvest Kids Praise Party 6 album, and has also released "The Mark Edwards Swing Gospel Jazz Orchestra" CD – performances that are rich and full of feeling, tenderness and power. Songs include "You Are Mighty", "Amazing Grace" and "Home Into Your Arms".

You are the hungry

Key = F

Mark Robins

Capo 5(C)

Gently ♩ = 68

You are the hun - gry,_____ You are all who__ thirst,

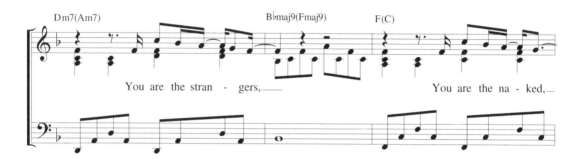

You are the stran - gers,_____ You are the na - ked,__

_ You are__ the sick,__ You are the pri - so - ners._____

So we want to be_____ Your__ hands,__ and we want to be__

You forgive then forget
(No condemnation)

Key = F

Capo 3(D)
Country rock

Brian Doerksen
& Philip Janz

1. You for-give____ then for-get,____ stones of hate____ You take our sins____ and cast____ them far - ther than the east is from____ the west.____ Our shame-ful past____ lost to You,____ our fu - ture found____ in Your____ com-pas - sion as we live out____ the truth.

as mer-cy tri - umphs o - ver judge - ment for that wo - man who____ re-mained.____ As love re - claims____ then re - stores,____ You mend our bro - ken hearts____ and make____ our lives stron - ger than____ be - fore.

Prayer of blessing

Baptising Spirit – send us out to be
hope-bringers to the tired and
the vulnerable.

Fire of the Spirit – send us out to be
sparks that rekindle the blaze of Your glory.

Fruitful Spirit – send us out like
branches as Your fruit-bearing people.

Gentle Spirit – send us out like doves as we
confront humanity's insecurities and fears.

And may the blessing of God, Father, Son and
Holy Spirit rest on us now and always. Amen.

© Marie Birkinshaw

You sent Your son
(Light the sky)

Key = A

Tim Hughes, Jamie Rodwell
& Sam Parker

Moderately

2. O-pen my eyes that I may see

1. You sent Your Son to make a way,

the won-der of Your ma-je-sty.

up-on the cross was all my shame;

And now I walk know-ing the truth:

Your fire of love will pu-ri-fy: it set me

free, it set me free. free.

You, I will fol-low— You———— to the ends of the— earth,—— ne-ver turn-ing

back. I will fol-low You, I will fol-low— You———— to the ends of the— earth,—

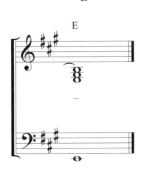

God of rescue and refuge; of shelter and strength. My still centre. My strong tower. When all is turning may I turn to You.

99 Your limitless majesty

Key = G

Ben Jones
& Sue Rinaldi

Steadily

1. Your li - mit - less ma - je - sty, Your
2. In view of this mer - cy I've found, my

beau - ty in all that I see; hum - bled I fall to my knees.
time on this earth in Your hands, I'll of - fer my life back to You.

Your mind has i - ma - gined my soul, Your
I long for Your king - dom to come, for

love and Your grace make me whole, Au - thor, per - fec - tor, my
all to be - lieve in Your Son, Your good - ness and grace to be

You're the giver of life
(Stand to sing)

Key = E

Capo 2(D)

Moderately; building

John Mongan
& Luke Gibson

1. You're the gi-ver of life, gi-ver of strength,
gi-ver of love, lo-ver of souls,

God of hope, God of my days.
Prince of peace,

2. You're the

3. God of my days. 2. You're the hope of the world.

Bridges to C

Bridges to D

From F

From G

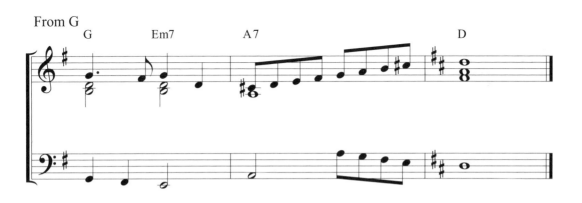

From B♭

From C

Bridges to E

From G

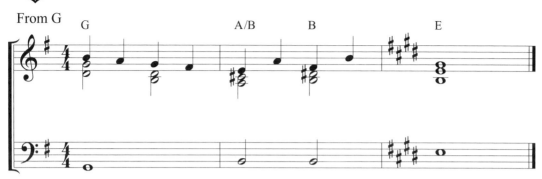

From A

From C

From D

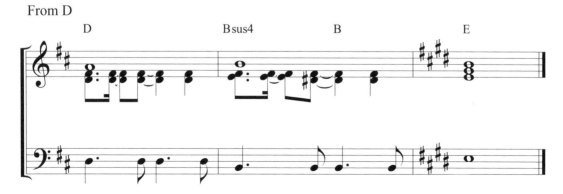

Bridges to F

From D

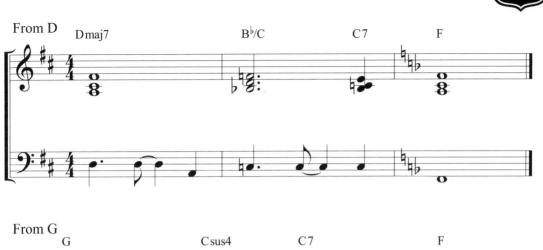

From G

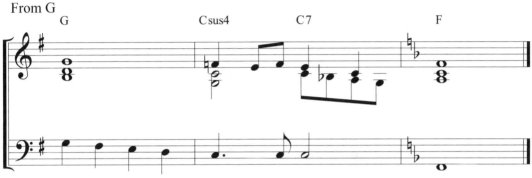

From B♭

From C

Bridges to G

Guitar Chord Charts

Roman	I	II	III	IV	V	VI	VII
Nashville	1	2	3	4	5	6	7

Key of D

	I	II	III	IV	V	VI	VII
3-note chord (triad)	D	Em	F♯m	G	A	Bm	C♯dim
4-note chord	Dmaj7	Em7	F♯m7	Gmaj7	A7	Bm7	C♯m7♭5
Alternative substitute	Dsus2	Em9	F♯m7	G6sus2	A7sus4	Bm11	Aadd9/C♯
Alternative bass note	D/F♯	Em/B	F♯m/A	G/B	G/A	Bm/F♯	

For all chords in the key of D♯ or E♭, use the chords from the key of D with capo 1

Key of E

	I	II	III	IV	V	VI	VII
3-note chord (triad)	E	F♯m	G♯m	A	B	C♯m	D♯dim
4-note chord	Emaj7	F♯m7	G♯m7	Amaj7	B7	C♯m7	D♯m7♭5
Alternative substitute	E5	F♯m11	G♯madd♭6	Aadd9	Badd4	C♯m7	D♯alt
Alternative bass note	E/G♯	F♯m/C♯	G♯m/D♯	A/C♯	A/B	C♯m/G♯	

For all chords in the key of F, use the chords from the key of E with capo 1

For all chords in the key of F# or Gb, use the chords from the key of E with capo 2

Guitar Chord Charts

Roman	I	II	III	IV	V	VI	VII
Nashville	1	2	3	4	5	6	7
Key of G 3-note chord (triad)	G	Am	Bm	C	D	Em	F#dim
4-note chord	Gmaj7	Am7	Bm7	Cmaj7	D7	Em7	F#m7♭5
Alternative substitute	G	A7sus4	Dsus4/B	Cadd9	Dsus4	Em7	G/F#
Alternative bass note	G/D	Am/C	Bm/D	C/G	C/D	Em/G	

For all chords in the key of G# or A♭, use the chords from the key of G with capo 1

Key of A 3-note chord (Triad)	A	Bm	C#m	D	E	F#m	G#dim
4-note chord	Amaj7	Bm7	C#m7	Dmaj7	E7	F#m7	G#m7♭5
Alternative substitute	Asus2	Bsus4	C#m7	D6sus2	Eadd9	F#m11	Eadd9/G#
Alternative bass note	A/E	Bm/F#	C#m/E	D/A	D/E	F#m/A	

For all chords in the key of A# or Bb, use the chords from the key of A with capo 1

For all chords in the key of B, use the chords from the key of A with capo 2

315

PROCLAMATION

Be Thou exalted
Before our God
First in pouring out Your love
First Word, last Word
God so loved
He is like no one
How great is Your love
I believe in You
I have a hope so sure
Jesus, You are strong to save
Lost are saved
Man of sorrows, Christ divine
O God of our salvation
Our hope is in You Lord
Over all he reigns
Shout the news
The air is filled with angels
The heavens declare
There is a King
Through You, the blind
will see
Water You turned into wine
We're not ashamed
Worthy is the Lamb
You are good
You're the giver of life

RENEWAL AND REFRESHMENT

I believe in You
I'm standing at the cross
In our hearts, Lord
More than just another song
Open my eyes again to see
Our God is mercy
Rain
The Lord is my shepherd
We wait in hope for you
What can separate me from
Your love?
When my soul is weak
You are God above the stars

RESPONSE

Brokenness has brought me
to my knees
Come alive
Deliverer, come set me free
From the thankful heart
Give me a heart of love
Here is love
How can we forget that he
has made his mercy known?
How could I not be on
Your side
I believe in You
I'm standing at the cross
I'm weak, You're strong
Jesus, take me as I am
May Your voice be louder
More than just another song
Open my eyes so I will walk
Overwhelmed
Spirit of God
These walls, these streets
What can separate me from
Your love?
What can we say?
When my soul is weak
You are God above the stars
You are the hungry
You sent Your Son
Your limitless majesty

SPIRITUAL WARFARE

Before our God
Deliverer, come set me free
He is like no one
I have a hope so sure
Jesus, thank You for the cross
(Power of the cross)
Jesus, You are strong to save
Lost are saved
Open my eyes again to see
Over all he reigns
Resting in Your promise
Through You, the blind
will see
Water You turned into wine
When my soul is weak

SUFFERING AND TRIALS

For you, the winter is past
From the thankful heart
I have a hope so sure
I love Your presence
I will give my whole self to
You Lord
Life could take
Man of sorrows, Christ divine
Our God is mercy
Praise Your name
Resting in Your promise
Stand, kneel, bow
The Lord is my shepherd
These mountains are high
Though I walk through waters
Through the love of God
our Saviour
What can separate me from
Your love?
When my soul is weak

SUITABLE FOR SOLO OR PRESENTATION

Brokenness has brought me
to my knees
Deliverer, come set me free
For you, the winter is past
Give me a heart of love
Give me eyes to see
I love Your presence
Life could take
More than just another song
Our God is mercy
The Lord is my shepherd

TRINITY

Be Thou exalted
O God of our salvation
To him who is able

Liturgy & Spoken Worship Index